Contents

Introduction 5

Seeking Eternity 6

AD 1857 Discovering the Tomb 17

Circa 1290 BC Building the Tomb 21

Circa 1550 to 1186 BC Burial in Egypt's Golden Age 22

Circa 1380 BC The Tomb of the Princesses next door 38

Circa 850 to 650 BC Reusing the Tomb 45

Circa 850 to 650 BC Burial in a Divided Egypt 56

Circa 30 BC to AD 10 Sealing the Tomb 61

30 BC to AD 300 Burial in Roman Egypt 78

Today Investigating the Tomb 80

The Tomb
Ancient Egyptian Burial

An exhibition at
National Museum of Scotland
Chambers Street
Edinburgh EH1 1JF

www.nms.ac.uk/thetomb

31 March to 3 September 2017

. . . .

Exhibition sponsored by
Shepherd and Wedderburn

Published in 2017 by
NMS Enterprises Limited – Publishing,
a division of NMS Enterprises Limited
National Museums Scotland
Chambers Street
Edinburgh EH1 1JF

www.nms.ac.uk

Text, photographs and illustrations
© National Museums Scotland 2017
(unless otherwise credited)

No part of this publication may be reproduced, stored in a retrieval system, or transmitted in any form or by any means, electronic, mechanical, photocopying, recording or otherwise, without the prior written permission of the publisher.

The rights of Margaret Maitland to be identified as the author of this book have been asserted by her in accordance with the Copyright, Designs and Patents Act 1988.

British Library Cataloguing in Publication Data
A catalogue record of this book is available from the British Library.

ISBN 978 1 910682 07 4

Book design by NMS Enterprises Limited – Publishing.
Printed and bound in the United Kingdom by Bell & Bain Limited, Glasgow.
Cover: Statue of the Chief of Police and his wife, Thebes, Egypt, c.1323–1279 BC (see page 21).
Cover design by Mark Blackadder, based on exhibition design.

For a full listing of NMS Enterprises Limited – Publishing titles and related merchandise:

www.nms.ac.uk/books

National Museums Scotland
would like to thank the following for their assistance in the publication of this volume:

Page 48 (left), Courtesy of Renfrewshire Leisure Limited on behalf of Renfrewshire Council; pages 5 (inscriptions), 16 (below), 38, 64 (inscriptions), © National Museums Scotland; pages 9, 19 (above), 22 and 41, © Margaret Maitland; page 77 (all), © National Museums Scotland and the University of Edinburgh; page 42 (fragments of decorative box of Amenhotep II), Acquired with Art Fund support and the support of the National Museums Scotland Charitable Trust.

Art Fund_

With many thanks to the curators, conservators, photographers, picture library and publishing staff, collections services, exhibition, design and administrative staff who have contributed to this book.

The Tomb

Ancient Egyptian Burial

Margaret Maitland

Saarah
Ellahi.

Goodword

Arabic

Writing

Book 4

M. Harun Rashid

GOODWORD

First published 2010
© Goodword Books 2010

Goodword Books
1, Nizamuddin West Market, New Delhi-110 013
E-mail: info@goodwordbooks.com
Printed in India

see our complete catalogue at

www.goodwordbooks.com
www.goodword.net

الله رب ۞ محمد رسول ۞ القرآن هداية

الله رب ۞ محمد رسول ۞ القرآن هداية

الله رب ۞ محمد رسول ۞ القرآن هداية

الله رب ۞ محمد رسول ۞ القرآن هداية

الله رب ۞ محمد رسول ۞ القرآن هداية

$\frac{8}{10}$

العلم نور ⁕ الإسلام دين ⁕ الرسول صادق

العلم نور ⁕ الإسلام دين ⁕ الرسول صادق

العلم نور ⁕ الإسلام دين ⁕ الرسول صادق

العلم نور ⁕ الإسلام دين ⁕ الرسول صادق

العلم نور ⁕ الإسلام دين ⁕ الرسول صادق

العلم نور ⁕ الإسلام دين ⁕ الرسول صادق

$\frac{6}{10}$

4

الله غنى ٭ الإنسان فقير ٭ النبى حق

5

10/10

18.6.14

الصلاة برهان ⋆ الصوم جنة ⋆ الصدقة ظل

الصلاة برهان ⋆ الصوم ⋆ جنة الصدقة ظل

الصلاة برهان ⋆ الصوم جنة ⋆ الصدقة ظل

الصلاة برهان ⋆ الصوم جنة ⋆ الصدقة ظل

الصلاة برهان ⋆ الصوم جنة ⋆ الصدقة ظل

الصلاة برهان ⋆ الصوم جنة ⋆ الصدقة ظل

✓ $\frac{10}{10}$ ✓

6

سبحان الله ۞ الحمد لله ۞ الله اكبر

سبحان الله ۞ الحمد لله ۞ الله اكبر

سبحان الله ۞ الحمد لله ۞ الله اكبر

سبحان الله ۞ الحمد لله ۞ الله اكبر

سبحان الله ۞ الحمد لله ۞ الله اكبر

سبحان الله ۞ الحمد لله ۞ الله اكبر

✓ 10/10 ✓

بلدة طيبة ⭐ رب غفور ⭐ رزق كريم

بلدة طيبة ⭐ رب غفور ⭐ رزق كريم

بلدة طيبة ⭐ رب غفور ⭐ رزق كريم

بلدة طيبة ⭐ رب غفور ⭐ رزق كريم

بلدة طيبة ⭐ رب غفور ⭐ رزق كريم

بلدة طيبة ⭐ رب غفور ⭐ رزق كريم

8

عذب فرات ❀ قول معروف ❀ أسوة حسنة

عذب فرات ❀ قول معروف ❀ أسوة حسنة

عذب فرات ❀ قول معروف ❀ أسوة حسنة

عذب فرات ❀ قول معروف ❀ أسوة حسنة

عذب فرات ❀ قول معروف ❀ أسوة حسنة

عذب فرات ❀ قول معروف ❀ أسوة حسنة

المسلم أخو المسلم ✶ الطهور شطر الإيمان

المسلم أخو المسلم ✶ الطهور شطر الإيمان

المسلم أخو المسلم ✶ الطهور شطر الإيمان

المسلم أخو المسلم ✶ الطهور شطر الإيمان

المسلم أخو المسلم ✶ الطهور شطر الإيمان

المسلم أخو المسلم ✶ الطهور شطر الإيمان

الحكمة ضالة المؤمن ۞ السواك مطهرة للفم

الحكمة ضالة المؤمن ۞ السواك مطهرة للفم

الحكمة ضالة المؤمن ۞ السواك مطهرة للفم

الحكمة

مفتاح الصلاة الطهور ⭐ مفتاح الجنة الصلاة

مفتاح الصلاة الطهور ⭐ مفتاح الجنة الصلاة

⭐

⭐

⭐

⭐

12

كل معروف صدقة ۞ خير الزاد التقوى

كل معروف صدقة ۞ خير الزاد التقوى

العجلة من الشيطان ✩ إنما المؤمنون إخوة

العجلة من الشيطان ✩ إنما المؤمنون إخوة

14

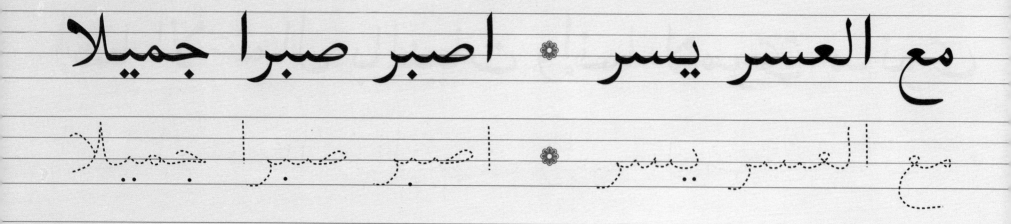

مع العسر يسر ۞ اصبر صبرا جميلا

إنما الأعمال بالنيات وإنما لامرئ مانوى

إنما الأعمال بالنيات وإنما لامرئ مانوى

طلب العلم فريضة على كل مسلم

طلب العلم فريضة على كل مسلم

إن الجنة تحت أقدام الأمهات

إن الجنة تحت أقدام الأمهات

18

الإيمان بضع وسبعون شعبة والحياء شعبة

الإيمان بضع وسبعون شعبة والحياء شعبة

القدوة الحسنة خير من الوصية

القدوة الحسنة خير من الوصية

إن الصدق يهدي إلى البر

إن الصدق يهدي إلى البر

إِنَّ البِرَّ يَهدي إِلى الجَنَّة

إِنَّ البِرَّ يَهدي إِلى الجَنَّة

إن الكذب يهدي إلى الفجور

إن الكذب يهدي إلى الفجور

إن الفجور يهدي إلى النار

إن الفجور يهدي إلى النار

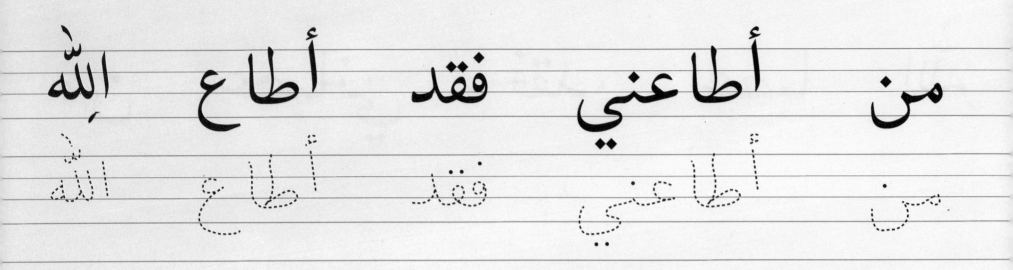

من أطاعني فقد أطاع الله

من عصاني فقد عصا الله

من عصاني فقد عصا الله

ليس منا من لم يرحم صغيرنا

ليس منا من لم يرحم صغيرنا

إن الله حرم عليكم دماءكم

إن الله حرم عليكم دماءكم

إن من خياركم أحسنكم أخلاقا

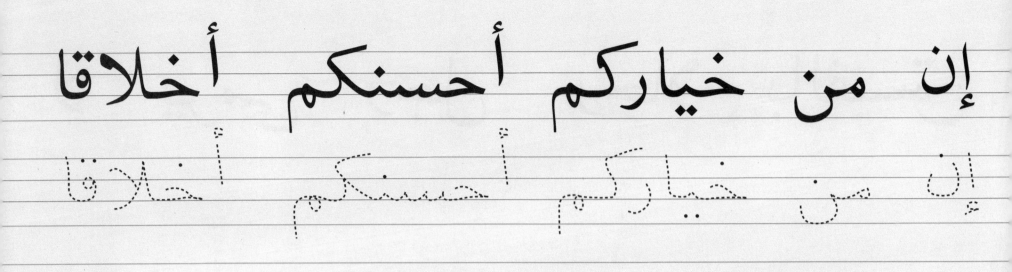

لا يرمي رجل رجلا بالفسق

لا يرمي رجل رجلا بالفسق

اللهم افتح لي أبواب رحمتك

اللهم إني أسئلك من فضلك

اللهم إني أسئلك من فضلك

يسلم الصغير على الكبير والمار على القاعد

يسلم الصغير على الكبير والمار على القاعد

ما يكسب بسهولة يضيع بسهولة

ما يكسب بسهولة يضيع بسهولة

إن تنصروا الله ينصركم ويثبت أقدامكم

إن تنصروا الله ينصركم ويثبت أقدامكم

النظافة أقرب شيء إلى التقوى

النظافة أقرب شيء إلى التقوى

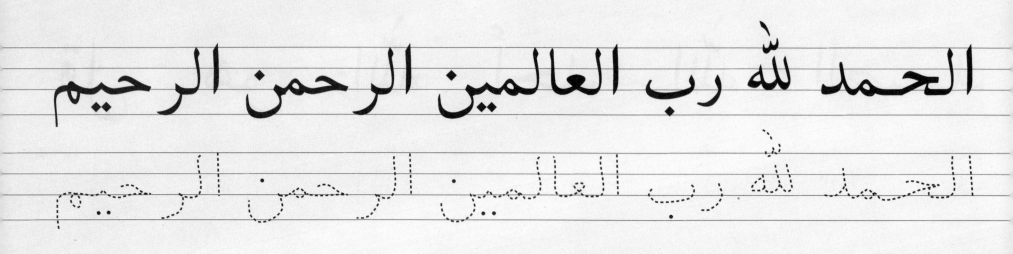

الحمد لله رب العالمين الرحمن الرحيم

قل هو الله أحد الله الصمد

قل هو الله أحد الله الصمد

لم يلد ولم يولد ولم يكن له كفوا أحد

لم يلد ولم يولد ولم يكن له كفوا أحد

إنا أعطيناك الكوثر فصل لربك وانحر

إنا أعطيناك الكوثر فصل لربك وانحر

الله لا إله إلا هو الحي القيوم

الله لا إله إلا هو الحي القيوم

إن الصلاة تنهى عن الفحشاء والمنكر

إن الصلاة تنهى عن الفحشاء والمنكر

ربنا آتنا في الدنيا حسنة وفي الآخرة حسنة

ربنا آتنا في الدنيا حسنة وفي الآخرة حسنة

قل ما عند الله خير من اللهو والتجارة

قل ما عند الله خير من اللهو والتجارة

سبح لله ما في السموات والأرض

سبح لله ما في السموات والأرض

سبح اسم ربك الأعلى الذي خلق فسوى

سبح اسم ربك الأعلى الذي خلق فسوى

الرحمن علم القرآن خلق الإنسان

الرحمن علم القرآن خلق الإنسان

ذلك الكتاب لا ريب فيه هدى للمتقين

ذلك الكتاب لا ريب فيه هدى للمتقين

Introduction

This is the extraordinary story of one tomb, carved into the desert cliffs opposite the Egyptian city of Thebes shortly after the reign of Tutankhamun in around 1290 BC.

It was intended to be the final resting place for the Chief of Police and his wife. But as Egypt's wealth and power declined, it was looted and reused several times over a period of a thousand years. The Tomb's final use occurred around 9 BC, soon after the Roman conquest of Egypt, when it was sealed intact with the remarkable burial of an entire family.

The Tomb was excavated in 1857, but was lost again as a village grew up over it. Today we are still learning about the Tomb from the objects found there.

Sandstone statue of the builder of the Tomb, the Chief of Police and his wife

On the back of the statue there are six columns of hieroglyphs. The column illustrated here on the left is an offering to Osiris for the Chief of Police in the afterlife.

Thebes, Egypt, *c.*1323–1279 BC

5

Seeking Eternity

The ancient Egyptians believed in the possibility of life after death. They thought of the afterlife as a continuation of life on earth, but potentially better.

In ancient times, short life expectancy meant death was an ever-present concern. The ancient Egyptians feared death, but hoped that it simply marked the next stage in existence. Egyptians hoped to join the sun god Ra in his eternal journey, to be reborn daily with the rising and setting sun.

They also wished to be like the god Osiris (right) who, according to myth, was the first person to be mummified. After Osiris died, he was brought back to life with magic by his wife Isis and sister Nephthys. He became king of the afterlife.

Ancient Egyptian beliefs in the afterlife remained constant, but burial practices changed over thousands of years, including different styles of tombs, evolving mummification practices, and a wide variety of funerary objects.

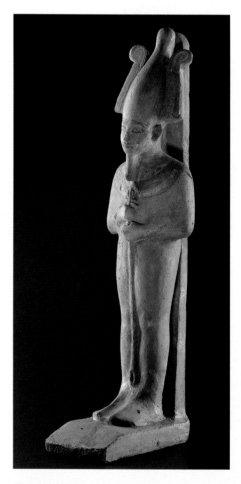

The god Osiris

This statue is one of a number that lined a processional route to the tomb of one of Egypt's first kings, who became identified with the god Osiris.

Statue of Osiris, clay, Umm el-Qa'ab, Egypt, c.1350–1187 BC

In prehistoric Egypt, belief in an afterlife began as early as around 4500 BC. Pottery vessels containing food and drink were placed in burials as provisions. The dead were buried in pits, usually laid facing west, towards the setting sun.

The sun's rebirth at dawn each morning was central to ancient Egyptian funerary beliefs. The pyramids, built as royal tombs, evoke the descending rays of the sun – a stairway to heaven – and were often given names with solar associations. The Great Pyramid was named 'The Horizon of King Khufu'.

The first funerary texts were inscribed on the walls of pyramid burial chambers in around 2400–2250 BC. These were magic spells intended to protect and reanimate the king's body so he could ascend to the heavens. These texts reveal that the deceased king also hoped to become like Osiris, ruler of the afterlife. This dual system of beliefs, relating to both solar and Osirian rebirth, characterised burial through the rest of ancient Egyptian history.

Royal pyramids were eventually abandoned in favour of the Valley of the Kings, but non-royal individuals adopted the form and built small pyramids above their tombs (page 22).

Opposite: Pyramidion of Mahu, a commander of the army

This top stone from a small pyramid above a tomb-chapel shows the sun travelling in a boat through the underworld to be reborn.

Limestone, probably Thebes, Egypt, c.1336–1186 BC

Below: The pyramids of Giza

Egypt, c.2580–2510 BC

For a person to be reborn in the afterlife, their soul had to undergo a divine transformation.

The *ba* was the part of a person's spirit that could travel out of the body, often represented as a human-headed bird (opposite). It was essential that the body was preserved to provide a resting place for the *ba* to return to each night.

The tomb itself had many roles; it protected the body, it aided in the divine transformation of the dead and provided for their soul in the afterlife. Tombs of the wealthy often had a decorated chapel for visitors and sealed underground chambers for the burial itself, containing many funerary objects. However, most people were buried simply in the ground with food and drink.

Relatives and priests often continued to bring offerings or to recite spells to magically invoke food for the dead's spirit. Each year, family would visit the tombs of their dead relatives to eat and drink with them.

Opposite: *Ba*-bird figurine
Wood, probably Akhmim, Egypt, c.664–332 BC

Below: Funerary banquet painting
Wall-painting from a tomb-chapel, painted plaster, Thebes, Egypt, c.1550–1400 BC

The mummification process preserved the body by drying it using natron, a form of salt, and wrapping it in linen. Oils, resins and beeswax were applied for fragrance and to aid preservation.

It was an expensive seventy-day process, accompanied by rituals performed by a team of priests, sometimes dressed as Anubis, the jackal-headed god of embalming. The priests recited spells intended to revive the dead and transform them into a divine being like Osiris.

Only the wealthy could afford to be mummified. Ordinary people were often simply wrapped in linen and buried in the ground.

Mummy label showing Anubis mummifying

The deceased is shown lying on a funerary bed.

Faience, Egypt, c.30 BC–AD 150

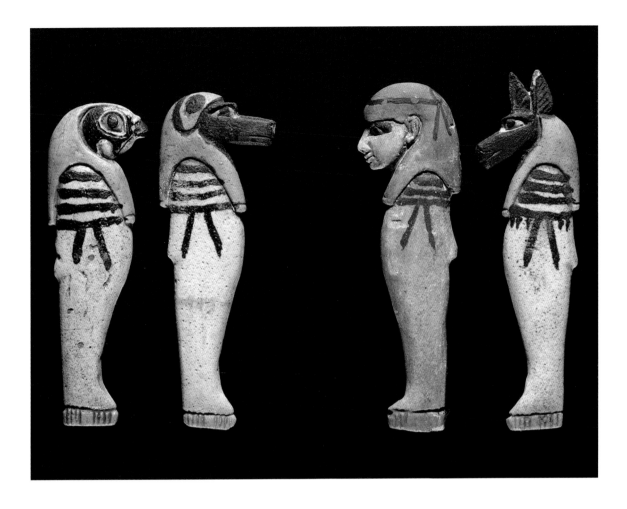

Sons of Horus

Amulets of the four Sons of Horus, faience, possibly Thebes, Egypt, *c.*1069–945 BC

The internal organs – the body parts most likely to decay – were often removed and mummified separately.

The Sons of Horus were gods responsible for protecting the internal organs. Earlier in Egyptian history, the organs were usually placed in protective canopic jars with lids featuring the heads of the Sons of Horus, but in later eras they were returned to the body accompanied by amulets like these.

Qebehsenuef was the falcon protector of the intestines.
Hapy was the baboon protector of the lungs.
Imsety was the human protector of the liver.
Duamutef was the jackal protector of the stomach.

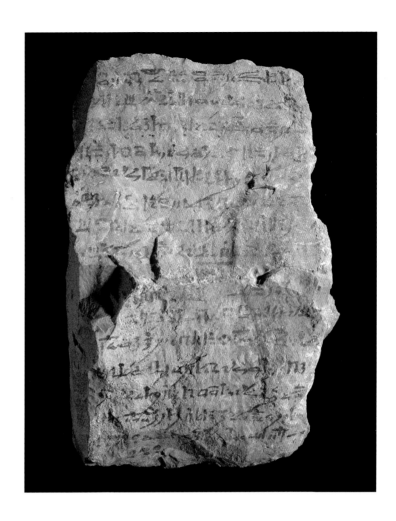

Right: Tomb warning

This rare example warns: 'I say to you, all people who will find this tomb-passage: Beware not to take even a pebble from it outside … [or] the gods of the West will reproach him greatly.'

Ostracon inscribed with a tomb warning, limestone, Thebes, Egypt, c.1295–1069 BC

Opposite: Ancestor bust

Limestone, possibly Deir el-Medina, Thebes, Egypt, c.1550–1186 BC

While the integrity of the tomb was important in securing the dead's continued existence and comfort in the afterlife, tomb curses were not common. The few that survive mostly just threaten legal action in the afterlife.

The tomb-chapel offered a place for family to visit and remember their relatives, but remembrance was also part of daily life in the home. The statue opposite was kept in a house, so that the family could remember and communicate with their dead loved ones. Egyptians believed that their deceased relatives who reached the afterlife could intercede with the gods on their behalf.

15

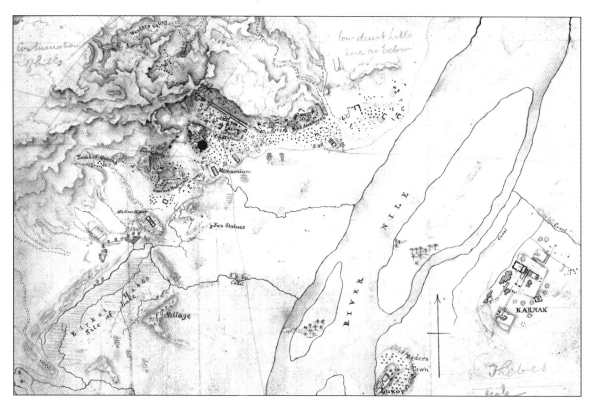

Ancient Egypt	The Tomb
c.3100 BC	
Unification of Egypt under the rule of one king	
c.2565 BC	
The Great Pyramid is built	
	c.1380 BC
	The tomb next door is built
c.1336–27 BC	c.1290 BC
Reign of Tutankhamun	The Tomb is built for the Chief of Police and his wife
c.1069 BC	
Egypt is divided between rulers in the north and the south	
	c.800 BC
c.747–656 BC	The Tomb is reused
Nubian kings rule Egypt	c.700 BC
	The Tomb is reused again
c.332 BC	
Alexander the Great conquers Egypt	
30 BC	
Roman forces defeat Cleopatra and Mark Antony and conquer Egypt	
27 BC–AD 14	9 BC
Roman Emperor Augustus rules Egypt	The Tomb is reused by high-official Montsuef and his family
	AD 1857
	The Tomb is rediscovered and excavated
	AD 2017

AD 1857

Discovering the Tomb

In the early 19th century, tomb looting in Egypt was common. Tombs were raided for objects to sell to collectors and museums. Archaeological recording of finds and their original locations were rarely made. This led to limited understanding of the original context of ancient Egyptian objects in museum collections.

In contrast, this Tomb on the west bank of Thebes was excavated systematically in 1857 by Scottish archaeologist Alexander Henry Rhind. He found a collection of beautiful objects from various eras, indicating that the Tomb had been used and reused over more than a thousand years.

Opposite, above: Draft map of Thebes by Alexander Henry Rhind, 1862
Showing the location of the Tomb in the cemetery at Sheikh Abd el-Qurna in red.

Opposite, below: Inset map of Egypt indicating the location of Thebes (modern Luxor)

Left: Timeline of the Tomb

Rhind made detailed records of the Tomb's layout and noted the exact locations of the objects he found. Although the connection of some of these objects to the Tomb was lost over time, recent research using the excavation notes and drawings has re-identified them.

Top: Section plan of the Tomb

The entrance corridor and curving sloping passageway measured about 38 metres. Objects discovered in the Tomb are illustrated on the plans, which were published in 1862.

Below: Plan of the Tomb's lower burial chambers

A shaft 6 metres deep led to five burial chambers extending a total of 17 metres. These had been reused since their construction and sealed with the intact burial of a Roman-era family.

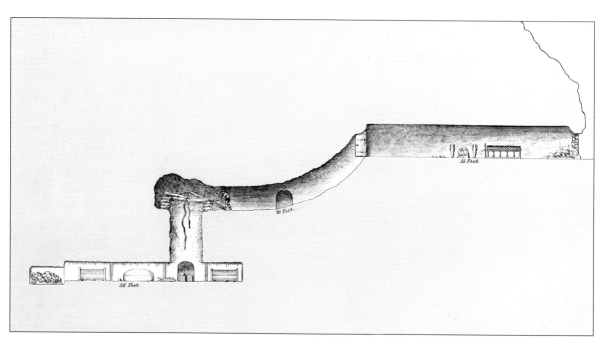

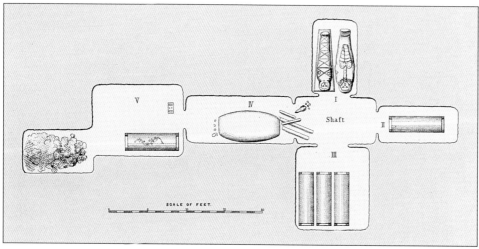

We know the approximate location of the Tomb from Rhind's archaeological records, but access has not been possible due to modern structures covering the site. Using Rhind's notes and drawings, one day it may be possible to rediscover it again.

Right: The location of the Tomb as it is today

Below: The location of the Tomb as photographed in 1857

Photograph taken near the location of the Tomb during the excavation in 1857 at Sheikh Abd el-Qurna on the west bank of Thebes.

Building the Tomb

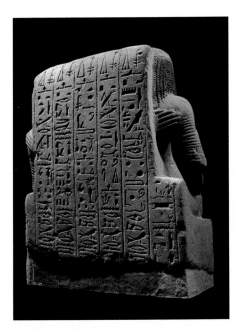

Chief of Police and his wife

On the back of the statue, five columns of hieroglyphs each describe a different god providing for the Chief of Police's afterlife: three local gods of Thebes and the gods of the afterlife, Osiris and his wife Isis. They offer bread, drink, breath and incense. The short column on the far right identifies the wife as 'beloved in his affection'.

Statue, sandstone, Thebes, Egypt, c.1323–1279 BC

The Tomb was constructed for a Chief of Police and his wife at the height of the ancient Egyptian empire, shortly after the reign of Tutankhamun.

Egypt controlled territories to both its north and south, and grew wealthy from the wide range of resources under its control. Pharaohs poured their riches into building enormous royal tombs in the Valley of the Kings. The high officials who helped run the country built hundreds of elaborate tombs opposite the capital city of Thebes. The Chief of Police was in charge of security forces who guarded these tombs, including the Valley of the Kings.

The construction of the Chief of Police's huge Tomb was expensive, but he saved on cost by using an existing courtyard built for an earlier tomb, where a group of princesses were buried. From the courtyard, a tunnel was carved 38 metres into the rock, followed by a burial shaft sunk six metres deep. The interior of the tomb was not decorated.

A beautiful statue of the Chief of Police and his wife is the only surviving object from their burial. They are shown as they wanted to be remembered, young and handsome, dressed in their finest pleated linen clothes and elaborate wigs. They sit with their arms affectionately around each other. Some original paint survives but the inscription is damaged, so their names do not survive.

Burial in Egypt's Golden Age

When Egypt was at its most prosperous and powerful, wealthy officials wanted to take their riches with them to the afterlife.

Tombs of the wealthy often had a decorated chapel for visitors and sealed underground chambers for the burial. The tomb served as a gateway between the world of the living and the world of the dead. Tomb-chapels were often richly decorated with images and words intended to memorialise the dead and help them reach the afterlife.

It could take years to construct and decorate an elaborate tomb and chapel. People often began preparing for their burial as soon as they could afford to. The wealthy filled their tombs with all the beautiful things that they enjoyed in life, from jewellery to furniture. Some economised by making miniature versions of daily-life objects specifically for burial. The display of wealth during the funeral procession to the tomb enhanced the status of the entire family.

People also bought protective magical objects, such as coffins, canopic jars and shabtis. These were inscribed with spells to protect the dead and aid their transition to the next life. Spells conferred knowledge, power and protection through means such as identification with different gods, magical wordplay, and directions guiding the deceased on the dangerous journey through the underworld to reach eternal paradise.

Above: Pyramid tomb-chapel

Reconstructed pyramid chapel of Sennedjem, made of mudbrick.

Deir el-Medina, Egypt, c.1280–1250 BC

Opposite: The Vizier Paser playing a board game

The Vizier Paser, who was the equivalent of prime minister under Ramesses II, is shown playing the board game *senet*, a scene from the Book of the Dead.

Tomb-chapel relief, Thebes, Egypt, c.1279–1213 BC

Taking it with you

Opposite: Eye makeup for both sexes, with mirror and comb

Wooden eye makeup container and applicator, Thebes, Egypt, c.1550–1186 BC; mirror, copper alloy, possibly from Thebes, Egypt, c.1550–1186 BC; comb, wood, Sedment, Egypt, c.1550–1295 BC

Below: Necklace with amulets

This colourful necklace was excavated in the burial of a young woman, but must have been worn during her lifetime. She may have collected the natural pebbles for good luck. The central amulet depicts the protective god Bes.

Various materials including faience, quartz, Gurob, Egypt, c.1481–1425 BC

Although only the Chief of Police's statue survives from this time period, these daily-life objects are similar to those that would have been placed in the Tomb. They are mainly from nearby tombs constructed at Thebes around the same time.

For adornment, the container opposite held black kohl eye-liner made from ground minerals. The shape imitates cheaper containers made of hollow reeds, but in a more expensive wood. Eye makeup was worn by men and women to enhance their appearance and possibly to protect the eyes against sun, flies and infection.

Combs were the main hair-care tool in ancient Egypt. Wealthy men and women often wore braided and curled wigs.

The surface of the mirror was originally highly polished and reflective. The handle is in the form of a papyrus stalk.

The larger of these two wooden boxes would have held precious personal items such as jewellery. The miniature version was made expressly for burial. It would be magically activated in the afterlife.

Large and small boxes

Box, wood inlaid with ivory or bone, Thebes, Egypt; and miniature version, Sedment, Egypt, c.1550–1186 BC

Wood was scarce in ancient Egypt. Only the wealthy could afford wooden furniture. Most people sat and slept on the floor on matting. The miniature stool (left) was a substitute made for burial.

Stool and model stool

Wooden stool with restored woven seat and model wooden stool, Thebes, Egypt, c.1550–1186 BC

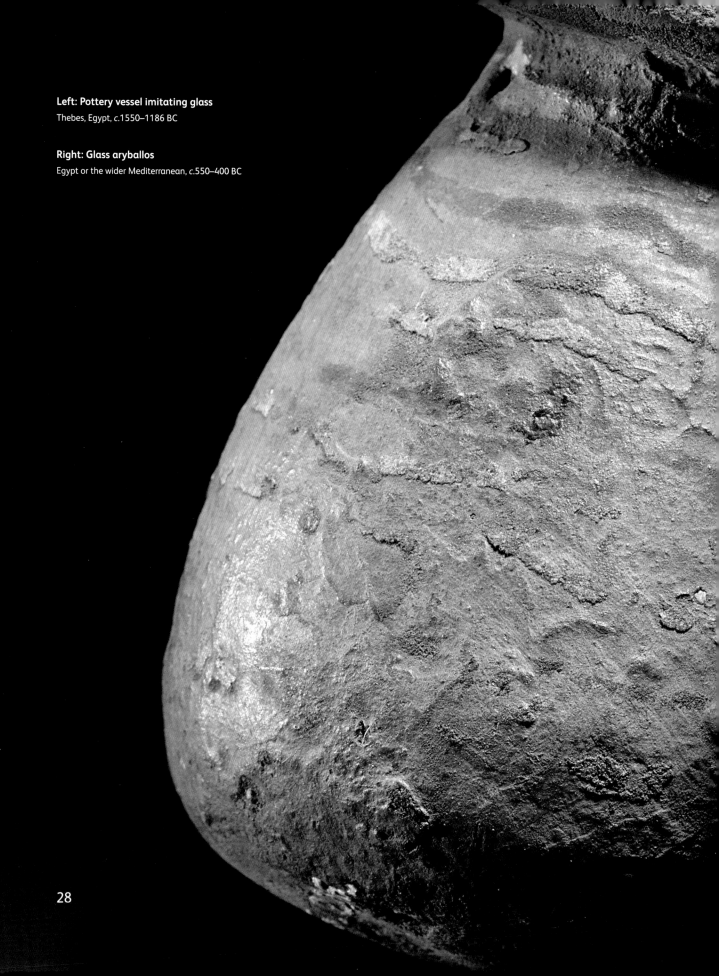

Left: Pottery vessel imitating glass

Thebes, Egypt, c.1550–1186 BC

Right: Glass aryballos

Egypt or the wider Mediterranean, c.550–400 BC

28

Glass was a relatively new invention in this period. Before the introduction of glass-blowing in the 1st century BC, the earliest glass vessels made in Egypt were formed by trailing molten glass around a core. They held scented oil or perfume.

The vessel on the left is a rare example of a ceramic jar painted with colourful stripes made to look like glass. As glass was expensive, this would have been a cheaper alternative.

29

Divine Transformation

Objects such as coffins, shrouds and amulets were made specifically for the burial to protect the body, transfigure the soul and aid the deceased's journey to the afterlife. Inscriptions were integral to this magic. The Egyptian term for hieroglyphs – *medu netjr* – means 'divine words'. The written word was believed to hold sacred power.

A coffin served to protect the body, but also aimed to transfigure the soul of the deceased. The lifelike realism of this coffin would have helped to bring its owner back to life. Tairtsekher died as an infant, but her coffin shows her as an adult so she could have a full life in the afterlife. She wears a fine linen dress, earrings, a necklace, bracelets, armlets and sandals. On the sides of the coffin, on bands that imitate mummy bandages, her name is written in hieroglyphs. 'Tairtsekher' means 'the one who was made according to a plan (of god)'. This inscription would have transformed the coffin into a substitute resting place for her soul.

Hieroglyphic writing is flexible and can be written in most directions. On the coffin, Tairtsekher's name and that of her mother Irtnefer, are written in vertical columns, as well as from left to right (opposite above) and right to left (below).

The magical funerary objects on the following pages are similar to those that would have been placed in the Tomb. They are mainly from nearby tombs built at Thebes around the same time (*c.*1550–1186 BC).

Right and opposite: Coffin of Tairtsekher
Wood, Deir el-Medina, Egypt, *c.*1295–1186 BC

31

One of the new innovations in this era was the introduction of the so-called Book of the Dead, a collection of magical spells that had developed out of texts written inside royal pyramids almost a thousand years earlier.

For the first time, these were written and illustrated on papyrus scrolls for the wealthy to take with them on their journey to the afterlife, as well as appearing on shrouds, amulets and shabtis.

Some spells guided the dead through potential dangers, using magic to transform perilous obstacles into empowerment of the deceased. For example, Spell 7 protects the dead against the snake Apophis, enemy of the sun god, who attempted to swallow the sun each night.

Other spells were intended to protect and sustain the body, especially the heart, which was believed to be the seat of all thought and emotion. Many of these aimed to restore the senses and reactivate the body's functions after death. For example (opposite page), the god Geb 'opens my eyes which were closed, he extends my legs … I shall have power in my heart, I shall have power in my legs'.

This fragmentary papyrus was found near the Tomb during its excavation. It was made for Useramun, a vizier (equivalent to prime minister) who served the female pharaoh Hatshepsut and Thutmose III, two of Egypt's most powerful rulers. The spells are beautifully written in columns of cursive hieroglyphs.

Above: Book of the Dead of Useramun, Spell 99

Useramun's name is repeated here with his many titles, including vizier, mayor of the city and sealbearer of the king.

Below: Spell 7

A spell for passing the dangerous coil of the snake Apophis. The title is written in red ink.

Opposite page: Spell 26

All papyrus, Thebes, Egypt, c.1479–1457 BC

In this period, mummified organs were stored in canopic jars. The Egyptians called these 'jars of embalming'. The lids were decorated with the protective Sons of Horus, depicted as human-headed (opposite). They later took on animal forms.

Some jewellery was made specifically for burial, usually serving a protective function. The two holes in the gilded wooden pectoral (above) originally held scarabs flanked by the goddesses Isis and Nephthys in a boat.

Amulets in the form of scarab beetles were commonly inscribed with a spell from the Book of the Dead. This spell was intended to prevent the heart from giving away any of the deceased's past bad deeds at their judgement before Osiris, which would determine entry to the afterlife. Scarab beetles were associated with the sun god and rebirth. The silt-stone scarab (below) still has a space left blank for the owner's name to be added.

Left: Pectoral

Wood, with linen, gesso and gilding, inlaid with glass, Sedment, Egypt, c.1550–1186 BC

Above: Heart scarabs

(Top) Heart scarab, serpentine, inscribed for Meryt, Egypt, c.1550–1186; (below) heart scarab, siltstone, Egypt, c.1550–1186

Opposite: Canopic jar of Priest Amunmose

Pottery, Sedment, Egypt, c.1479–1352 BC

Shabtis were intended to serve as substitutes, in case the dead were called up by conscription to do physical labour in the afterlife.

Shabtis were generally depicted as mummiform, holding tools, and inscribed with a magical spell to activate them in the afterlife: 'O shabti … if I be summoned to do any work in the realm of the dead … cultivating the fields, irrigating the banks, or conveying sand from east to west, "here I am," you shall say.'

Originally just one shabti was placed in a burial, but the number grew over time, eventually needing a box to hold them. This one (below, right) shows the owner, Tamery, standing before Osiris and Isis. Osiris is depicted with green skin, symbolic of life and rebirth. The reverse (opposite page) shows a tree goddess, probably Hathor, pouring water for Tamery, who kneels before an offering table. The sides are decorated with figures of the Sons of Horus.

Below, left: Shabti of Ramessesnakht

This example had its original owner's name erased and replaced with the name Ramessesnakht.

Wood, Thebes, Egypt, *c.*1295–1186 BC

Below and opposite: Shabti box of Tamery

Wood, Thebes, Egypt, *c.*1295–1186 BC

The Tomb of the Princesses next door

Another tomb was discovered beside the Tomb of the Chief of Police and his wife.

Inside was the burial of a group of princesses, including daughters of King Thutmose IV. The tomb was looted in ancient times, but a beautiful gilded ebony and ivory box (pages 42–43) offers a glimpse of royal wealth and splendour.

Wooden name-tags recorded their names for eternity. Ancient Egyptians believed that preservation of the name was important for survival in the afterlife. Some of these wooden labels may have been attached to the mummified princesses. Their names are written with black ink in a cursive form of hieroglyphs called hieratic: Tiaa and Pyihia, daughters of King Thutmose IV, Nebetia, daughter of Prince Saitem, Tataw, Pypwy, Henwtiunw, Ptahmeryt, Sathori, Neferuamun and Wiay.

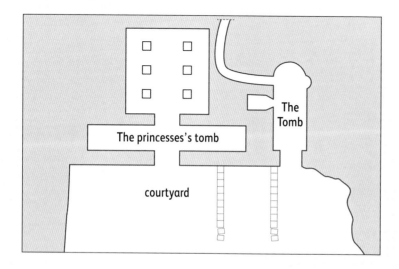

The princesses's tomb

The Tomb

courtyard

Left: Plan of The Tomb (right) with the tomb of the princesses beside it (left)

Opposite: Wooden labels inscribed for princesses

Wood, Thebes, Egypt, c.1390–1352 BC

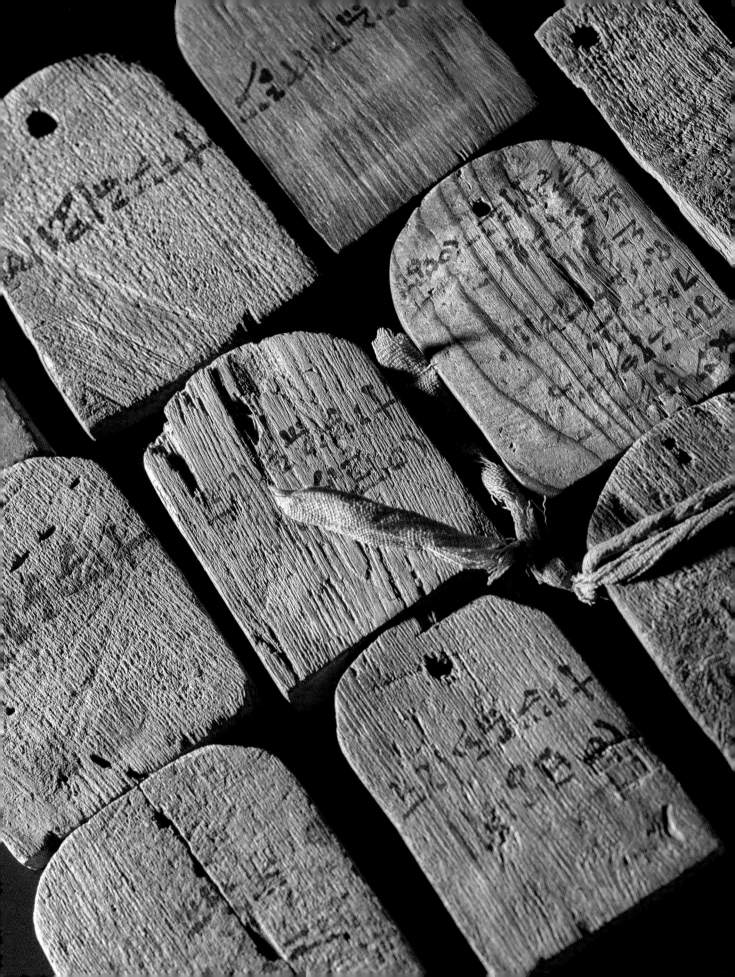

At the height of Egypt's powerful empire, foreign leaders sent tribute to Egypt, sometimes including their daughters to be married to the pharaoh. Kings often had several wives and many children.

The style of the statue head opposite suggests that it may represent King Amenhotep II, grandfather of the princesses. He is shown wearing a cloth royal headdress with a uraeus (royal cobra) on his brow.

In the scene below, princesses perform purification rituals before King Amenhotep III in celebration of his jubilee. They present vessels of gold and electrum containing cool water.

Opposite: Statue head of a king, possibly Amenhotep II

Basalt, Egypt, *c.*1479–1390 BC

Below: Princesses

Relief in Theban Tomb 192 of Kheruef, Thebes, Egypt, *c.*1390–1352 BC

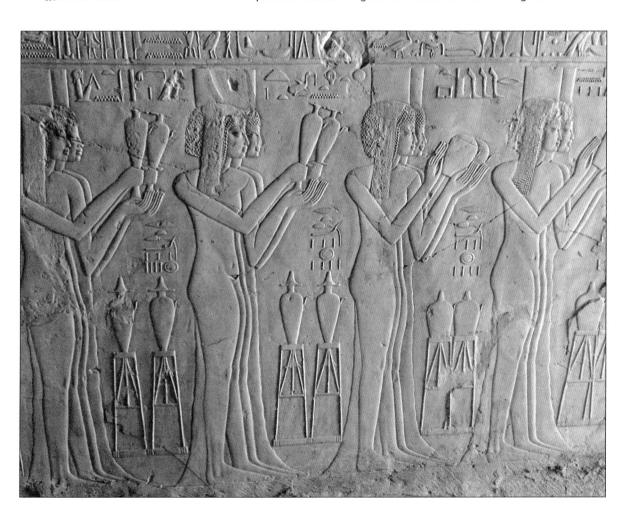

This box is a masterpiece of ancient Egyptian craftsmanship. Decorated with the ferocious protective god Bes, it may have originally held cosmetics.

A rich array of royal symbolism adorns the box, including papyrus plants, emblematic of Egypt itself. The name of Amenhotep II inscribed on an ivory plaque sits above the hieroglyph for 'gold', framed by notched palm ribs, used to record the length of a king's reign, on top of hieroglyphs for 'eternity'. The box is made of cedar wood imported from Lebanon with delicate ebony and ivory veneers from further south in Africa, as well as gilding.

Fragments of the box were missed during the original excavation. They were recently rediscovered and acquired by the Museum. They show that the lower band of decoration on the box was incorrectly restored in the 1950s. The original pattern symbolises the royal palace.

Decorative box of Amenhotep II and associated fragments

Featuring the protective god Bes.

Cedar, ebony, ivory, gold, Thebes, Egypt, c.1427–1400 BC

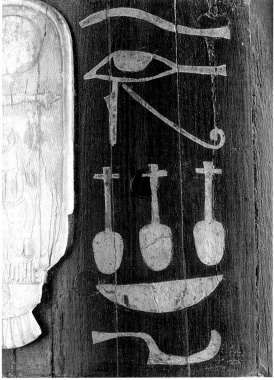

Circa 850 to 650 BC

Reusing the Tomb

Above and opposite (detail): Stela of the Lady of the House Takai

Wood, Thebes, c.850–747 BC

Egypt's fortunes changed as it lost control of its empire. It went into decline, weakened by war and famine. The north and south were divided between competing pharaohs. Then Egypt was conquered by Nubia (modern Sudan). Without their former wealth, Egyptians economised in their burial preparations and reused everything from coffins to tombs.

We do not know how long the Tomb of the Chief of Police remained intact, but it was eventually reused. Reuse did not necessarily entail desecration; often earlier burials were simply moved aside. Several small, roughly-carved chambers were probably added to the upper level of the Tomb to hold additional burials. Repeated looting left behind a confusing jumble of broken coffins and scattered burial items by the time the Tomb was discovered.

The remnants of objects from the Tomb's reuse can date the burials to at least two instances between 850 and 650 BC. Two stelae suggest that a woman named Takai and a Gatekeeper of Amun named Sennu may have been among the first to reuse the Tomb. Guardian figures from the lids of lost coffins date to a later period of reuse and can help to reconstruct what the coffins looked like.

Most of the objects on the following pages were found in the upper chambers of the Tomb. The connection of some to the Tomb is still uncertain because the early Museum descriptions and records were quite basic. Together these objects offer clues about when the Tomb was reused and by whom.

The objects buried with some of the first people to reuse the Tomb include wooden stelae (pages 44–47) that commemorate the dead, showing them worshipping the falcon-headed sun god Ra-Horakhty. In this period, the sun god surpassed Osiris in importance in funerary beliefs. The stelae belong to a woman named Takai, a Gatekeeper of Amun named Sennu, and an unknown woman.

Several black outer-coffins dating to this period were found damaged in the Tomb, but not brought back to the Museum. This suggests several people were buried there in plaster and linen mummy-cases like the one illustrated on page 57.

Above and opposite (detail): Stela of an unknown woman

Her name does not survive as the column of hieroglyphs containing her name is damaged. The god Thoth is shown pouring water over her for purification.

Stela, wood, Thebes, *c.*825–715 BC

Left: Stela of the Gatekeeper Sennu

The stela represents the cosmos in miniature, framed by standards bearing the hieroglyphs for 'east' and 'west', with an overarching 'sky' hieroglyph and the winged sun disk.

Stela, wood, Thebes, *c.*850–747 BC

Objects from the Tomb's reuse also reveal changes in mummification practices.

With widespread tomb looting and reuse, ancient Egyptians worried that organs stored in canopic jars might become separated from the body. Solid dummy canopic jars were still made for tradition's sake and symbolic protection, but organs were returned to the body. These were found in the entrance corridor of the Tomb.

A small statue of Osiris was a new addition to burials. The hieroglyphs describe him as a 'great god', 'Foremost of the Westerners [the afterlife gods]'. Later, statues of Osiris combined with other afterlife gods as 'Ptah-Sokar-Osiris' became a common feature of burials, often serving as a container for funerary papyri.

The objects shown here, and on the following pages, date to the second, later period of reuse, when Egypt was under Nubian rule.

Below, left: Dummy canopic jars

The human- and falcon-headed lids represent Sons of Horus, Imsety and Qebehsenuef, who protected the liver and intestines.

Limestone, Thebes, *c.*747–656 BC

Below and opposite: Figure of Osiris

The statue was left unfinished and is missing the owner's name.

Wood, Thebes, Egypt, *c.*747–656 BC

Opposite and below: Box of clay shabtis

Box, wood; shabtis, clay, Thebes, Egypt, *c.747–656 BC*

Shabtis changed from a substitute for the dead to a whole workforce who served them.

The number in a typical burial increased to 365, one for each day of the year, plus 36 overseers. However, these huge groups were usually of poor quality. The tiny mummiform figures, only a few centimetres high, were mass-produced from mud in moulds. The shabti box also became smaller and simpler. It was typically decorated with a funerary prayer to Ra-Horakhty with a ship painted on the lid.

Jackal figure
Wood, Thebes, Egypt, c.747–525 BC

52

Guardian figures such as this one and the ones on pages 1 and 54 represent protective jackal and falcon gods. They were found in the chamber off the entrance corridor to the Tomb.

These figures hint at larger objects that did not survive as they were originally attached to coffin lids. This form of coffin harked back to an earlier style shaped like a god's shrine with four posts and a vaulted lid, which would have helped to transform the dead into an eternal being.

Above: Model coffin

Probably from a Ptah-Sokar-Osiris statue. The heads of the jackal and falcon are reconstructed.

Wood, Egypt, c.747–525 BC

Opposite: Guardian figure of a falcon

Wood, Thebes, Egypt, c.747–525 BC

The protective falcon figure (opposite) would have been attached to a now lost full-sized coffin lid. The mummiform falcon represents Sokar, a god of the underworld who became closely associated with Osiris.

Rhind described finding these objects in the Tomb's upper chambers, which had been looted in antiquity: 'Among the *débris* … were several painted funeral tablets of wood of the usual character, boxes that had contained sepulchral clay images, wooden jackals, hawks, [and] the common upright swathed figures on pedestals.'

The model coffin (above) does not come from the Tomb, but it gives a sense of what the lost full-sized coffins would have looked like with jackal and falcon figures on the lids.

Circa 850 to 650 BC

Burial in a Divided Egypt

After Egypt lost control of its empire, the country became divided. The powerful high priests in Thebes, such as Pinudjem, proclaimed themselves kings of the south.

Then, around 747 BC, kings of Nubia took control of Egypt. They brought stability to a reunited Nile valley and appointed the defeated Egyptian rulers as provincial governors. They built and restored many temples to the Egyptian gods. Nevertheless, Egypt's wealth was no longer what it once was.

The political and economic changes in Egypt were reflected in burials, as people looked to cut costs. Objects from daily life were generally no longer placed in the tomb. Statues and decorated tomb-chapels became rare. Instead, the dead were commemorated on small painted wooden stelae. Abbreviated versions of the Book of the Dead were introduced, consisting of a single sheet rather than a roll, with just one illustration. Since wood was scarce and expensive, a cheaper form of mummy-case was invented made from linen and plaster (opposite). Nevertheless, the painted decoration is often incredibly elaborate.

The objects presented on the following pages are similar to those that may have been buried with the individuals who reused the Tomb between 850 and 650 BC.

Above: King Pinudjem I

Shabti of High Priest and King Pinudjem I, faience, Thebes, Egypt, c.1054–1032 BC

Below: Nubian King of Egypt and Nubia

Statuette, bronze, Saqqara, Egypt, c.747–656 BC

Opposite: Mummy-case of the priest Nehemsumut

Plaster and linen (cartonnage), Thebes, Egypt, c.840–815 BC

A standard mummy-case was cheaper than one that was commissioned and designed especially for you. The footboard (below) is from a mummy-case that was probably bought 'off-the-shelf', since the name of the dead man, Pamiu, 'The Cat', was added later in different handwriting.

The decoration depicts a mummified man being symbolically transported on the back of the protective Apis bull to his tomb, which is shown surmounted by a small pyramid.

In this period, protective shrouds placed over the mummified body were introduced, made of faience beads (quartz-based ceramic). The face shows the dead transformed into Osiris, whose blue-green colour evokes fertility and rebirth.

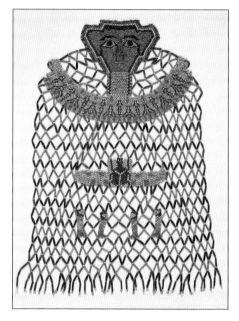

Opposite, above: Bead-net shroud

Faience, Egypt, *c.*332–30 BC

Opposite, below: Mummy-case foot-board of Pamiu

Wood, Thebes, Egypt, *c.*790–750 BC

Below: Eye of Horus plaque

Amulet, silver, Egypt, *c.*1069–656 BC

During this period, internal organs were mummified and then returned to the body. The Sons of Horus continued to protect the organs in the form of amulets wrapped with them, made of wax or faience (page 13).

Organs were traditionally removed via the left side of the torso. The Eye of Horus amulet was placed on the incision to magically heal it so the body would be whole again. According to myth, the eye of the god Horus had been injured by his usurping uncle but was then restored, and the amulet below was intended to invoke sympathetic magic.

Sealing the Tomb

The Tomb's last reuse was by the high-ranking local official Montsuef and his family. They lived through the reign of the last pharaoh Cleopatra. Cleopatra was descended from one of the generals of Alexander the Great, who had brought Greek rule to Egypt in 332 BC.

Montsuef's family witnessed Egypt's conquest in 30 BC by the soon-to-be first Roman Emperor Augustus. Under Roman rule, classical influence increased, but southern Egypt where Montsuef lived held on to many Egyptian traditions.

Montsuef's father had been the local governor and his family was very wealthy. They came from Armant, 12 miles south of Thebes, but they chose the ancient, sacred Theban cemetery as their final resting place.

The unique objects from their burials combine new classical influences with traditional Egyptian funerary practices. Items such as Montsuef's funerary canopy and bilingual papyri reinvented ancient traditions and reasserted the family's Egyptian identity in their search for eternal life.

Funerary canopy of Montsuef
Sycomore wood, Thebes, Egypt, 9 BC

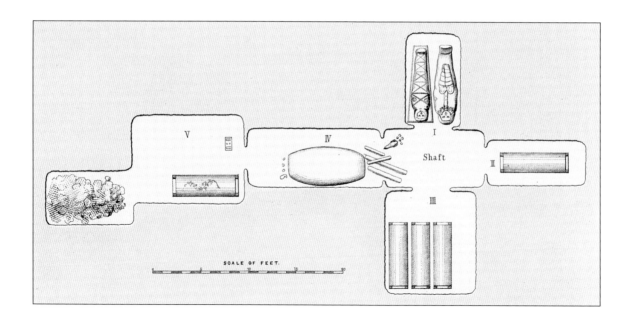

Above: Plan of the lower chambers of the Tomb, originally published in 1862

The Tomb's lower chambers were left undisturbed for almost two thousand years, preserving a remarkable assemblage of burial objects.

Montsuef's family added an iron lock to the Tomb in order to open and close it securely. Over time, eight adults and three children were added to the lower chambers before the Tomb fell out of use.

The five lower chambers each held between one and four mummified individuals, buried mostly in wooden coffins, wrapped in painted shrouds and inscribed bandages, with amulets and funerary papyri. Because this assemblage was recorded in context and can be dated to 9 BC specifically by inscriptions on the papyri, the Tomb's artefacts are important for understanding and dating other Roman-era funerary objects.

Below: Fragment of mummy bandage inscribed for Montsuef (detail)

Mummy bandages inscribed with protective spells were typically written in cursive hieratic or demotic. Montsuef's uses hieroglyphs, an older form of writing perceived as more sacred and powerful. At least six meters of inscribed bandage were wrapped around Montsuef.

Linen, Thebes, Egypt, 9 BC

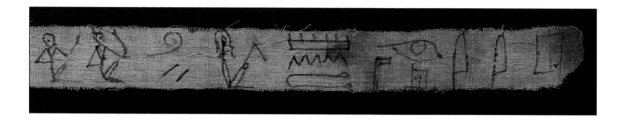

The central chamber of the Tomb (Chamber IV) was occupied by Montsuef's massive granite sarcophagus, roughly chiselled and undecorated. Beside it lay rollers that had been used to move it into position.

Within the sarcophagus was the mummified body of Montsuef covered in resin embedded with amulets, wrapped in a shroud and inscribed mummy-bandages, and wearing a gold wreath over a gilded mask. Beside the sarcophagus were a mummified jackal, ibis, falcon and snake. These may have replaced the traditional canopic jars featuring the animal-headed Sons of Horus. In the doorway to the chamber lay a tall amphora filled with doum palm fruits. These were the only provisions found in the Tomb, so it may be that the fruits held a symbolic value, possibly promoting rebirth.

Chamber II was the only one sealed by a wooden door. It contained a large plain wooden coffin with a vaulted lid inscribed for a man named Kalasiris. In Chamber III were three similar plain vaulted wooden coffins. One contained Tanuat, wife of Montsuef, while the others may have held their son and daughter. Another vaulted wooden coffin in Chamber V was festooned with crumbling green branches. In a corner was a reused stone offering table. At the far end was another unfinished room filled only with stone chips.

Chamber I held a plain tapered wooden box with no lid, containing a mummified individual in a painted shroud, and a reused anthropoid coffin with the bodies of a man and young girl. On top of this coffin was a dried wreath and two infants, loosely wrapped together. These remains were very different from the lavish burial goods found in the other chambers, so they may have been later additions.

Left: Mummified woman (see pages 76–77)

Found in Chamber III or V, this mummified woman may be Tanuat's daughter, but this will not be known until the funerary papyrus within her mummy wrappings can be read.

Human remains, linen, beeswax, resin, with amulets of mixed materials, Thebes, Egypt, c.20 BC–AD 10

Family Tree of Montsuef and Tanuat

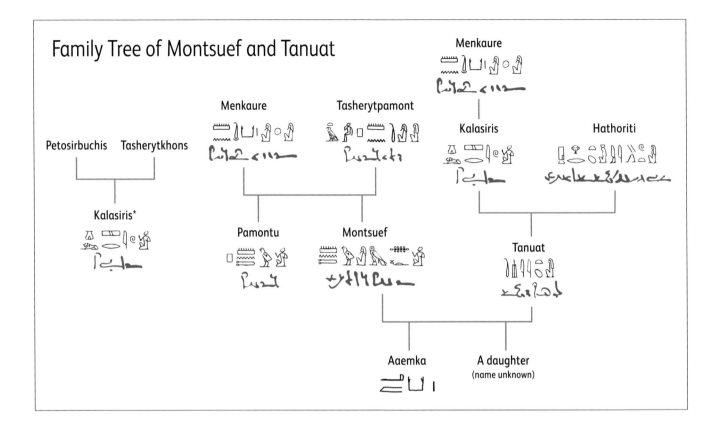

Objects found in the Tomb were inscribed with details about Montsuef and Tanuat's family relationships and professional titles. Not all of these individuals were buried in the Tomb.

Montsuef was a high-official (*syngenes*) and cavalry officer. His father Menkaure was the local governor and military general (*strategos*) of the city of Armant and a priest of Montu-Ra and other gods.

Tanuat was a high-ranking woman who married Montsuef. She was buried with two coffins beside her, probably her son and daughter. Tanuat's father Kalasiris was a high-official (*syngenes*) and a priest of Montu-Ra.

Pamontu was Montsuef's brother and succeeded their father as *strategos*. He was buried in the reused sarcophagus of Ankhnesneferibra, daughter of King Psamtek II, in the basement of a house at Deir el-Medina.

Kalasiris*

On one end of the lid of this coffin there is an inscription in demotic (a late cursive script) that begins: 'You will live and your name will live.'

Below: Coffin of Kalasiris
Wood, Thebes, Egypt, c.30–10 BC

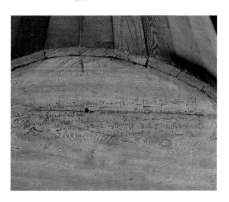

This coffin belonged to Kalasiris*, son of Petosirbuchis and Tasherytkhons, a military officer and presumably a relative of Montsuef, although the exact relationship is not clear. It was left undecorated apart from the inscription. The text goes on to describe how Kalasiris will be received by Osiris in the afterlife, while his *ba* will go forth with the sun god at dawn and rest upon his body in the evening.

When the Tomb was found, the wooden beams and rope used to lower this coffin and others into the lower chambers were still in place.

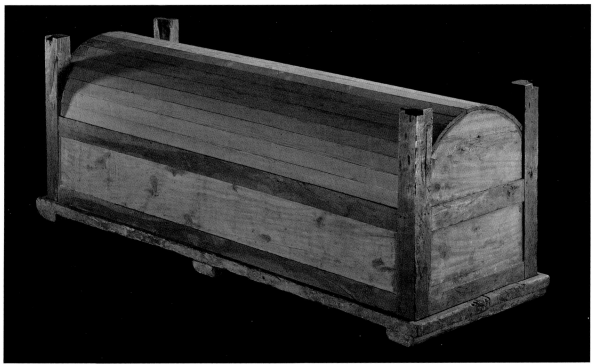

Funerary Canopy of Montsuef

The canopy probably protected Montsuef's body during his transportation to the Tomb. Since he was interred in a granite sarcophagus placed in the Tomb beforehand, his body needed protection during the funeral procession. It was then left in the entrance corridor of the Tomb.

Funerary canopy of Montsuef
Sycomore wood, Thebes, Egypt, 9 BC

The canopy is shaped like an Egyptian temple to aid Montsuef's divine transformation. The criss-cross decoration on top evokes a protective bead-net shroud. This unique new object is unprecedented in the history of ancient Egyptian burial; the closest comparable objects are funerary beds, used during the mummification process. Nevertheless, its form in the shape of an Egyptian temple, with royal cobra and winged sun-disk motifs, is entirely traditional.

Mummy-masks, such as Montsuef's on the opposite page, were often gilded or painted yellow because Egyptians believed the skin of the gods was made of gold.

According to a new practice introduced in this period, the skin of Montsuef's mummified body was also gilded to help to transform him.

A classical-style gold wreath was placed on top of Montsuef's traditional mummy-mask. The laurel wreath was a classical symbol of victory, reinterpreted in Roman Egypt as a symbol of triumph over death. Egyptians may have also associated it with the 'crown of justification', awarded to the virtuous in the earlier Book of the Dead.

Opposite: Mummy-mask of Montsuef
Gilded plaster, glass, Thebes, Egypt, 9 BC

Below: Wreath of Montsuef
Wreath of leaves, gold-foil, attached to gilded copper ring, Thebes, Egypt, 9 BC

Funerary Papyrus of Montsuef

Unlike earlier standardised funerary papyri, those of Montsuef and his wife Tanuat are unique, personalised with details about the good lives they led to justify their entry into the afterlife.

Notably the inscriptions are bilingual, written in two cursive scripts: older hieratic, which had religious precedent, and contemporary demotic.

The papyrus of Montsuef records that he was born on 4 December 69 BC and died on 4 July 9 BC. His life is described as long and happy: 'You attained a great age on earth. You drank and ate there. You did all that your heart desired.'

The text instructs Montsuef to 'call out in a loud voice: "O my lord, my father Osiris! I am an excellent man .... Nor have I committed a sin, your abomination, in my lifetime".'

Funerary papyrus of Montsuef (detail)

Amidst funerary gods, the mummified body of Montsuef is shown lying in his coffin in the protective embrace of the sky goddess Nut. Above, his spirit departs in the form of a *ba*-bird.

Papyrus, Thebes, Egypt, 9 BC

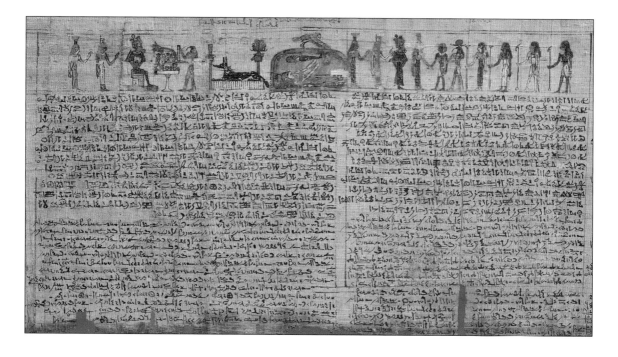

These papyri are also important sources of evidence for the mummification process, documenting many of the steps and rituals.

Some of the text was likely recited by the priests performing the embalming: for example, 'The voice of Anubis as he speaks to Montsuef: Welcome to us, one who has come exhausted to the necropolis … I will lay my hands upon your body as I do for my father Osiris. I will make your limbs sound, for I am Anubis in my guise as lector priest'.

The text states that 17 processions will be made for Montsuef within the 70 days of mummification, in which 103 litres of sacred ointment will be boiled for him. It addresses Montsuef, describing details of the process: 'Your wrapping, consisting of the bandages of the gods and goddesses. Anubis as lector priest filling your skull with Syrian resin, incense, myrrh, and cow's fat …. Amulets of every precious stone, silver and gold in plenty will be tied on for you.'

Below: Funerary papyrus of Montsuef (detail)

Montsuef is shown lying on a mummification bed. The two jackal-headed figures represent the god Anubis. Priests who performed the embalming sometimes wore a jackal-mask.

Papyrus, Thebes, Egypt, 9 BC

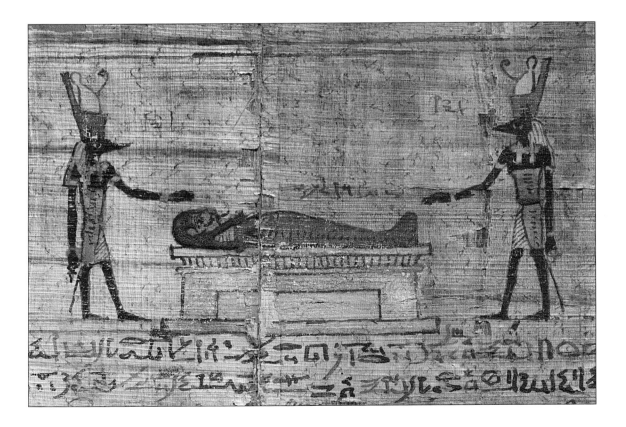

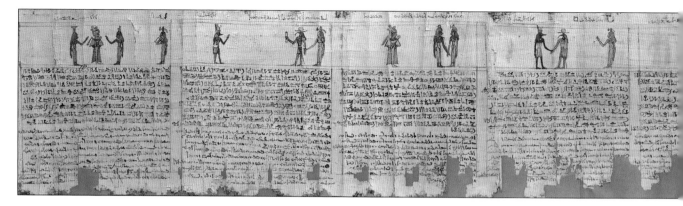

Above: Funerary papyrus of Tanuat

The roll measures just over 2.1 metres. The inscription is written in columns that are read from right to left.

Papyrus, Thebes, Egypt, 9 BC

Below: Funerary papyrus of Tanuat (detail)

Tanuat (far right) is shown transformed into a sanctified being, wearing a lotus-flower – symbol of rebirth – and a cone of perfume. She is led by Anubis to Osiris, flanked by Isis and Nephthys.

Papyrus, Thebes, Egypt, 9 BC

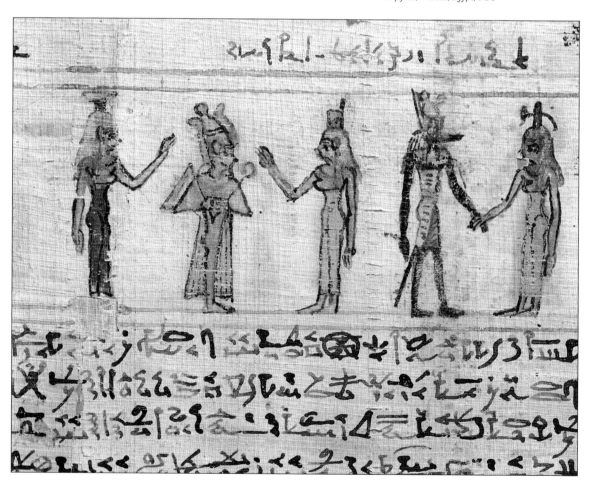

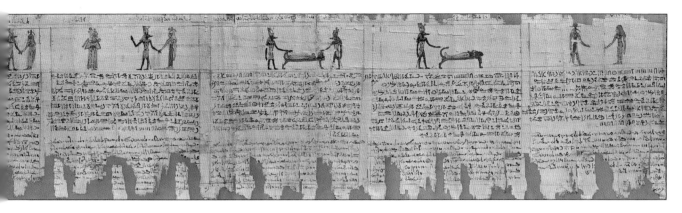

Funerary Papyrus of Tanuat

Tanuat's birth date is recorded as 31 May 62 BC and is described as 'the happy day of the birth of a good woman'.

Above: Funerary papyrus of Tanuat (details)

Both rolls are preserved to their full length, with Montsuef's papyrus measuring over 2.7 metres in length and Tanuat's 2.1 metres. Tanuat's papyrus (above) is a shortened version of her husband's and the spells are adapted to suit her. Unlike her husband, who is called 'the Osiris Montsuef', Tanuat is referred to as 'Hathor', the goddess of fertility and rebirth.

Tanuat became a mother herself and the text welcomes her to the afterlife as 'one of the happy women … having completed your span of living with a pleasant life on earth. You left a son and daughter behind you, one succeeding another in the house of your father.'

Tanuat's arrival in the afterlife is celebrated on account of her virtue: 'Those who are in the afterlife say "Praised be you" to you upon your arrival at the hall of the West because of the greatness of your virtues in the sight of everyone. Your good deeds will be recited in the presence of Osiris. He will favour you eternally.'

She died aged 54 on 21 August 9 BC, just 48 days after her husband.

The son of Montsuef and Tanuat, Aaemka, is shown transformed into the god Osiris. He wears Osiris' crown and false beard, and holds his symbols of power, the crook and flail. Across his brow is a frieze of royal cobras.

Egyptian art usually depicted people in profile, but the attempt to model Aaemka's features here may have been influenced by the realism of classical art. Its unusual style seems to represent a transitional phase between earlier Ptolemaic bead-net shrouds and later Roman Osirian shrouds.

The criss-cross bead-net pattern was traditionally protective. The red dye colouring was probably associated with the sun and rebirth. His feet are shown exposed, perhaps to ensure his ability to stand upright and come and go in the afterlife.

On either side, gods are depicted in protective poses: Isis and Nephthys, the goddesses who brought Osiris back to life, and two jackal figures representing Anubis, god of mummification.

The hieroglyphic inscription down the centre addresses him with 'Hail the Osiris Aaemka, son of Hemsaf [an alternative spelling of Montsuef] and Tanuat'.

Right and opposite (detail): Mummy-shroud of Aaemka, son of Montsuef

Linen, Thebes, Egypt, *c.*20 BC–AD 10

Mummified Woman

This woman (see page 63) was a member of Montsuef's family. CT scanning has allowed us to see beneath her wrappings.

The scans revealed an amulet hidden within the wrappings on top of the woman's head. The amulet is made from a thin sheet of metal, probably either silver or gold. 3D printing was used to create the replica below, right. The hidden amulet is located almost directly below another amulet of a similar design. The winged scarab represents the newborn sun god at dawn and hope for rebirth in the afterlife.

The young woman was five feet two inches tall. Her teeth and bones tell us that she was aged between 20 and 35.

The CT scan also revealed that she has a rolled-up funerary papyrus placed at her right-hand side. With emerging developments in scanning technology, it is hoped that the papyrus will eventually be able to be read and her name discovered. The papyrus is probably similar to Montsuef's and Tanuat's, containing detailed information about who the woman was, and when she was born and when she died.

Below, left: Detail of the mummified woman's head

A *djed*-pillar amulet representing the backbone of Osiris was placed on her forehead for stability. On either side, Eye of Horus amulets conferred healing.

Human remains, linen, beeswax, resin, amulets of mixed materials, Thebes, Egypt, c.20 BC–AD 10

Below: Replica 3D printed amulet printed by the University of Liverpool

Titanium, gold, Liverpool and Edinburgh, United Kingdom, AD 2012

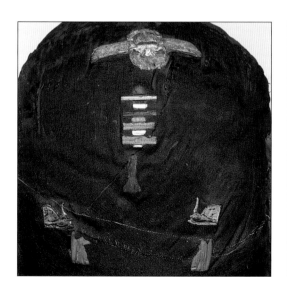

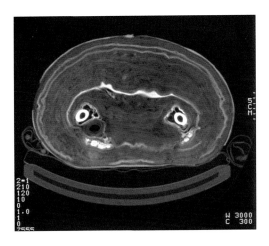

Above: CT scan section of the legs of the mummified woman

CT scan revealing the hidden papyrus roll.

Right: CT scan of the mummified woman

Carried out by the Clinical Research Imaging Centre at the University of Edinburgh. The amulet on the opposite page can be seen on top of the woman's head.

Below: CT scanning of the mummified woman

Carried out by the Clinical Research Imaging Centre at the University of Edinburgh.

Human remains, linen, resin, amulets of mixed materials, Thebes, Egypt, c.20 BC–AD 10

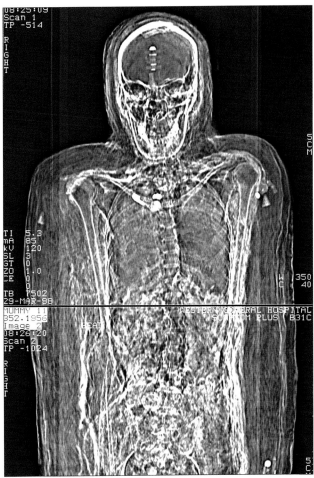

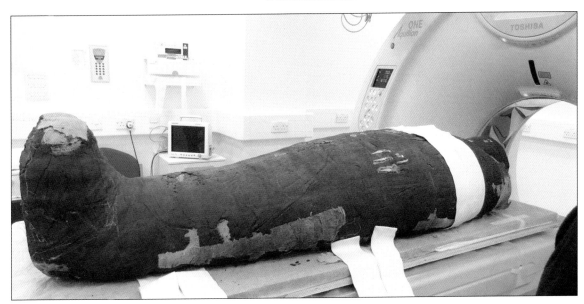

30 BC to AD 300

Burial in Roman Egypt

By the time Egypt became part of the Roman Empire, its burial traditions and religious beliefs were already thousands of years old. Egypt was increasingly influenced by classical culture, but in matters of death, many people looked to the reassurance of traditional magic.

Burials now focussed almost entirely on the body itself. Funerary objects like shabtis and canopic jars completely disappeared. Even coffins became rare. The most commonly used burial items were shrouds and either an Egyptian-style mummy-mask or a classical-style portrait painted on a board placed over the face of the mummified person. Traditional-style gilded mummy-masks were decorated with magical protective symbols and Egyptian gods. Classical portraiture sought to bring the dead back to life through its realism.

Objects from this period demonstrate how much Egypt was being transformed by external influence, but also just how determined the Egyptians were to hold onto their traditions in their pursuit of the afterlife.

Shrouds decorated with ancient Egyptian symbols continued to be produced until around the late third century AD. However, with the introduction of Christianity and then Islam, the burial practices of pharaonic Egypt were finally abandoned. Nevertheless, the ancient Egyptians still live on today, given eternal life through their extraordinary burial objects.

Above: Roman period mummified man with portrait

Linen, wood, plaster (cartonnage), human remains, Hawara, Egypt, c.AD 80–120

Opposite: Roman period mummy-mask

Linen and plaster (cartonnage), gilding, Hawara, Egypt, c.30 BC–AD 120

Investigating the Tomb

The discovery of the Tomb in 1857 was the beginning of the next chapter in its story. Its excavation and recording were innovative for the time, which has enabled contemporary research to reconstruct its history.

We have rediscovered objects from the Tomb in the Museum's collection, as well as in museums in Paisley and Durham. These have broadened our understanding of ancient Egypt's changing burial practices. The Roman-era burials of Montsuef and his family challenge our perceptions of ancient Egyptian identity.

With future advances in scanning technology, it will be eventually possible to read the name of the mummified woman on the papyrus within her wrappings (pages 76–77).

Although the location of the Tomb has been lost, one day it may be found again. Until that day, there is still much we can learn from its objects as they slowly reveal the Tomb's secrets.

Detail of eye from the mummy-mask of Montsuef

Gilded plaster, glass, Thebes, Egypt, 9 BC